Gleat's Pas Heg

Bill Caldwell
CARTOONS

Pedigree BOOKS

Published by Pedigree Books Limited
The Old Rectory, Matford Lane, Exeter, Devon, EX2 4PS.
Under licence from Express Newspapers plc.
Printed in Italy. © 1993 Express Newspapers plc.

£3.95

D0333002

CA 4

"Not much wrong with this environment"

DAILY STAR, Tuesday, June 2, 1992

'At least there's a guaranteed sunbed.'

DAILY STAR, Friday, June 5, 1992

'No . . really . . there's no need to kneel'

DAILY STAR, Wednesday, June 10, 1992

DAILY STAR, Wednesday, June 17, 1992

'...then when we ring the dinner bell, they all eat each other'

DAILY STAR, Thursday, June 18, 1992

'One more grunt and they're both off'

DAILY STAR, Tuesday, June 23, 1992

DAILY STAR, Friday, June 26, 1992

DAILY STAR, Monday, June 29, 1992

"Fined and barred"

DAILY STAR, Wednesday, July 1, 1992

'. . . And if you look to your left you will see the Marquis relaxing with wifelets nine and ten.'

DAILY STAR, Thursday, July 2, 1992

DAILY STAR, Monday, July 13, 1992

'Quite a holiday atmosphere building up, Prime Minister, don't you think?'

DAILY STAR, Thursday, July 16, 1992

'Go on, Nigel — take the hat off'

DAILY STAR, Tuesday, August 18, 1992

BILL CALDWELL

DAILY STAR, Friday, August 21, 1992

"I think you've got 10 Downing Street, dear"

DAILY STAR, Thursday, August 27, 1992

"Cheer up — you could be in Balmoral"

DAILY STAR, Monday, August 31, 1992

"At the moment the French seem evenly divided between 'Oui' and 'Non'"

DAILY STAR, Friday, September 4, 1992

'Sure I've got mice in the kitchen – what about it?'

DAILY STAR, Wednesday, September 9, 1992

'I know the Germans are being a pain, Norman - but we can't just bomb the Bundesbank'

DAILY STAR, Tuesday, September 15, 1992

"Shouldn't we leave a note or something?"

DAILY STAR, Thursday, September 17, 1992

"Look, Norman, they've made a film about us already"

DAILY STAR, Tuesday, September 22, 1992

'We thought we'd a-have him a-stuffed while he's still in a-one piece'

DAILY STAR, Friday, September 25, 1992

'Of course we haven't got a TV licence – who'd want to watch this ****?'

DAILY STAR, Thursday, October 1,1992

'Business? Couldn't be better'

DAILY STAR, Wednesday, October 7, 1992

"I wouldn't go there if I were you, sir"

DAILY STAR, Thursday, October 8, 1992

"Got everything? Armour? Asbestos suit? Flame thrower?"

DAILY STAR, Friday, October 9,1992

DAILY STAR, Tuesday, October 13, 1992

'Are you quite sure this is what you want, miss?'

DAILY STAR, Wednesday, October 14, 1992

DAILY STAR, Friday, October 16, 1992

"How thoughtful — they're sending us lumps of coal for the winter"

DAILY STAR, Monday, October 19, 1992

'Will you be paying in Pounds or Deutschmarks, Your Majesty?'

DAILY STAR, Tuesday, October 20, 1992

"How did we get here? Underground to Trafalgar Square then straight down Whitehall"

DAILY STAR, Thursday, October 22,1992

'Aw shucks, honey – you know I need every vote I can get.'

DAILY STAR, Tuesday, November 3, 1992

"Congratulations, Mr President — hope to meet you soon, all being well"

DAILY STAR, Wednesday, November 4, 1992

"Penny for the Euro-rebels"

DAILY STAR, Thursday, November 5, 1992

'Foreign aid, Mr Yeltsin? Sign here — how much will you give us?'

DAILY STAR, Tuesday, November 10, 1992

'Ohmygosh – Whatever next?

DAILY STAR, Wednesday, November 11, 1992

'So THAT'S your Autumn Statement?'

DAILY STAR, Thursday, November 12, 1992

'Rest assured, sir - we're sending details of your mortgage reduction as quickly as possible'

DAILY STAR, Tuesday, November 17, 1992

'Gained a few pounds, I see'

DAILY STAR, Wednesday, November 25, 1992

"Lend us a tenner"

DAILY STAR, Friday, November 27, 1992

'HOW MUCH?!'

DAILY STAR, Wednesday, December 2, 1992

"Storm? Non, Monsieur, ze farmers are at it again"

DAILY STAR, Thursday, December 3, 1992

"Of course it's bound to be a bit difficult at first"

DAILY STAR, Thursday, December 10, 1992

"Mmmm . . . love this one — do you do it in red?"

DAILY STAR, Friday, December 11, 1992

DAILY STAR, Thursday, December 17, 1992

"Could you charge it to the DSS?"

DAILY STAR, Tuesday, December 22, 1992

'I don't blame them'

DAILY STAR, Friday, January 1, 1993

'I think he's picked up Saddam.'

DAILY STAR, Tuesday, January 19, 1993

'The invitation said wear white'

DAILY STAR, Tuesday, January 26, 1993

'...and *THAT* will cost you £20,000!'

DAILY STAR, Wednesday, January 27, 1993

"Smoking's just not worth the risk — there goes another one"

DAILY STAR, Thursday, January 28, 1993

'What's the problem? You've still got the mascot, haven't you?'

DAILY STAR, Friday, January 29, 1993

"That looks like a private one coming now"

DAILY STAR, Wednesday, February 3, 1993

'I see they've started the work-for-dole already'

DAILY STAR, Friday, February 5, 1993

'Ignore it – it's a mirage.'

BILL CALDWELL

DAILY STAR, Tuesday, February 9, 1993

'I see England are getting the runs at last'

Bill Caldwell

DAILY STAR, Friday, February 12, 1993

'Gosh! For a horrible moment I thought it was Charles.'

DAILY STAR, Tuesday, March 2, 1993

"It was that one"

DAILY STAR, Wednesday, March 3, 1993

"I'll never forget his last words — 'HOW MUCH?!'"

DAILY STAR, Thursday, March 4, 1993

'By the way - there's no money left for parachutes'

DAILY STAR, Monday, March 8, 1993

"Come to bed, Norman — if you don't understand it now, you never will"

DAILY STAR, Monday, March 15, 1993

DAILY STAR, Thursday, March 18, 1993

'I don't like the look of this, Boris'

DAILY STAR, Tuesday, March 23, 1993

"Not THAT much freedom, Mr Clough"

DAILY STAR, Wednesday, March 24, 1993

"Just thought you'd like to know it's 3am and all's well, Mr Clarke"

DAILY STAR, Thursday, March 25, 1993

'Most people stop and say a few words'

DAILY STAR, Wednesday, March 31, 1993

"Go easy now — he's needed for the National tomorrow"

DAILY STAR, Friday, April 2, 1993

"Well, we broke his legs, then we had to put him down."

DAILY STAR, Monday, April 5, 1993

'Here's an idea .. why don't you go on strike while the kids are off school?'

DAILY STAR, Tuesday, April 13, 1993

'We've been called in to keep Thatcher and Major apart.'

DAILY STAR, Thursday, April 15, 1993

'Forget it Lloyd - you'll never make the weight, son'

DAILY STAR, Friday, April 16, 1993

'Asil Nadir? Never heard of him - I'm Graeme Souness'

DAILY STAR, Thursday, May 6, 1993

'WHERE TO? CYPRUS?'

DAILY STAR, Monday, May 10, 1993

'I got them in a charity shop.'

DAILY STAR, Tuesday, May 11, 1993

'Ahem! I think you'll find the problem is *electronic* bugs, sire'

"Right! Now..can we talk?"

"Er..could we just have something to eat?"

DAILY STAR, Monday, May 17, 1993

'No, honestly – the *red* outfit looks *fine*'

DAILY STAR, Tuesday, May 18, 1993

'Told you that would clear her throat'

DAILY STAR, Monday, May 24, 1993

'When you're finished . . . '

DAILY STAR, Wednesday, May 26, 1993

"As you can see, we've got Colonel Bob in a safe haven.."

DAILY STAR, Thursday, May 27, 1993

'Expecting more stick, Mr Taylor?'

DAILY STAR. Wednesday, June 9, 1993

'Mr Taylor, isn't it? I've been a great admirer of yours for many years'

DAILY STAR, Friday, June 11, 1993

'Great here innit? Somebody said these seats weren't needed'

DAILY STAR, Thursday, June 17, 1993

'I think they're pleased with the new batons, Home Secretary'

DAILY STAR, Friday, June 18, 1993

"Oi! There's a queue"

DAILY STAR, Tuesday, June 22, 1993

'Your courtesy car has arrived, Miss Graf'

DAILY STAR, Thursday, June 24, 1993

'Looks like we've won'

DAILY STAR, Friday, June 25, 1993

'Bad luck he was the 100th person to say *"That's Life"*, Esther'

DAILY STAR, Monday, July 5, 1993

'This driving ban's really going to hurt old Woosie'

DAILY STAR, Tuesday, July 6, 1993

'I can never remember their names'

DAILY STAR, Monday, July 26, 1993

'Spare a tenner?'

DAILY STAR, Friday, July 30, 1993